THIS BOOK BELONGS TO:

THIS BOOK BELONGS TO:

Write your name above
the blue line and use the
grid to draw its reflection
underneath (see pages 24-25).

THIS IS NOT ANOTHER MATHS BOOK

IVY KIDS

Anna Weltman

Illustrated by Charlotte Milner

First published in the UK in 2017 by

Ivy Kids

An imprint of The Quarto Group
The Old Brewery
6 Blundell Street
London N7 9BH
United Kingdom
www.QuartoKnows.com

British Library Cataloguing-in-Publication Data
A catalogue record for this book is available from the British Library.

ISBN: 978-1-78240-498-9

This book was conceived, designed & produced by

Ivy Kids

58 West Street, Brighton BN1 2RA, United Kingdom

PUBLISHER Susan Kelly
CREATIVE DIRECTOR Michael Whitehead
MANAGING EDITOR Susie Behar
ART DIRECTOR Hanri van Wyk
IN-HOUSE DESIGNER Kate Haynes
PROJECT EDITOR Leah Willey
EDITORIAL ASSISTANT Lucy Menzies
DESIGNED AND ILLUSTRATED BY Charlotte Milner

Manufactured in Guangdong, China TT082020

5 7 9 10 8 6 4

MIX
Paper from
responsible sources
FSC® C016973

CONTENTS

Maths and Art.

THEY HAVE NOTHING IN COMMON
...OR DO THEY?

Maths is the study of patterns and symmetry.

And what is more beautiful than a symmetrical snowflake?

Or more decorative than an intricate pattern?

MAYBE MATHS AND ART HAVE A LOT MORE IN COMMON THAN YOU THINK.

If you ask any
mathematician why they love maths, they're
likely to say, 'Because maths is beautiful!'. With a little
bit of creativity, you can transform numbers and shapes into
fascinating patterns and designs. Use some clever folding and cutting to
make delicate paper snowflakes (pages 60-63), and turn simple lines and
curves into tangled-up knots (pages 46-47). Want to hold infinity in the palm of
your hand? Make a three-dimensional fractal (pages 32-33). Want to trick your
friends with some mathe-magic? Try a geometric vanish puzzle (pages 18-21).

TRY THE ACTIVITIES IN THIS BOOK AND SEE HOW MATHS CAN BE ART, AND ART CAN BE MATHS!

Once you learn how to do an activity, try it on your own - either
in the book or on another piece of paper. Don't forget the
extra graph paper at the back of the book!
What beautiful maths can you make?

YOUR TOOLBOX

YOU ONLY NEED A FEW THINGS TO MAKE SMART MATHS ART:

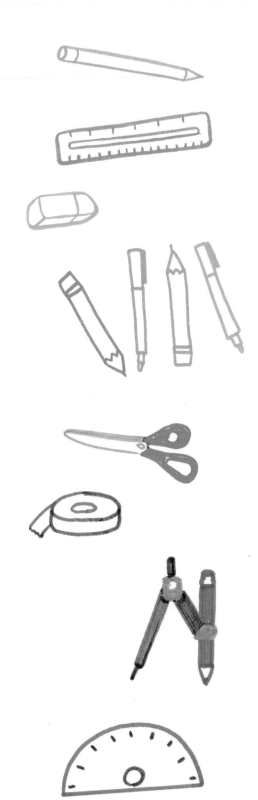

PENCIL: use a pencil for your first go, just in case you want to erase anything and have another try.

RULER: use a ruler whenever you need to draw perfectly straight lines.

ERASER: use an eraser if you need to have another try at any of the activities or to erase any bits of drawings that you don't need.

COLOURING PENCILS OR PENS: use colouring pencils or pens to decorate your smart art.

SCISSORS: sometimes you'll need to cut out shapes. Use a small pair of scissors.

TAPE: ordinary sticky tape is all you need.

COMPASS: this tool is essential for drawing perfect circles. It looks like a V. On one leg of the V, there's a pencil, and on the other leg, there's a spike. You stick the spike into your paper, so that you can swing the pencil around a central point.

PROTRACTOR: use this to draw angles. One edge is flat but the other edge is curved to form half a circle, and marked with degrees – the unit of measurement used to describe angles – from 0° to 180°.

PLAIN PAPER: use plain paper to draw on or for projects where you want to cut out shapes.

TRACING PAPER: if you're asked to trace shapes, tracing paper is useful (you could use greaseproof paper). You can then trace your shape back onto regular, plain paper if you need to.

GRAPH PAPER: this is paper marked with a square or triangular grid. You'll find some at the back of the book.

ANGLES: if you don't have a protractor, you can still do all of the activities that require one by using these angle pieces. Trace them, cut them out and use them whenever you need an angle!

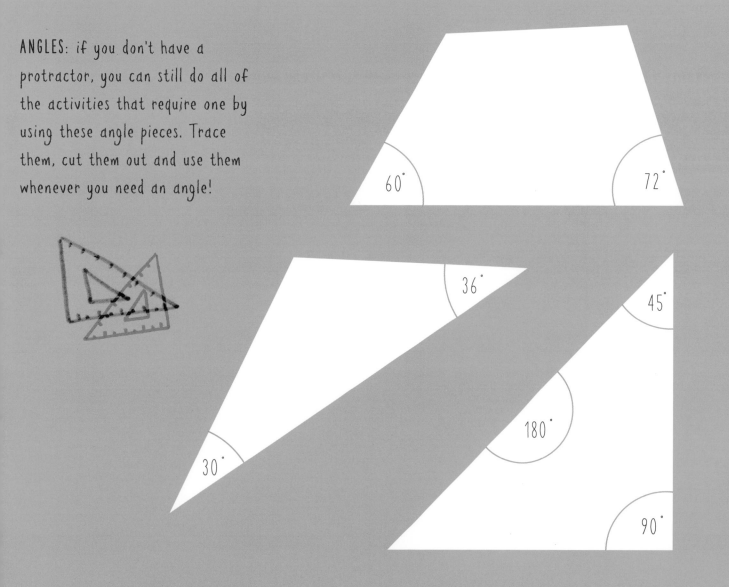

LINE BASICS

TO DRAW THESE SPECIAL LINES, YOU NEED THREE OF A MATHEMATICAL ARTIST'S FAVOURITE TOOLS — A RULER, A COMPASS AND A PENCIL.

Perpendicular lines

Two lines are perpendicular if they cross each other at a right angle. They are important when you're making mathematically perfect pictures, and they're oh-so-easy to draw.

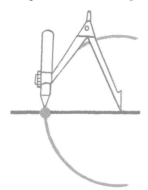

Place your compass point here ·····▸

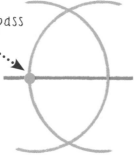

PERPENDICULAR LINES!

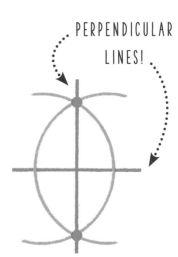

1 Using a ruler, draw a straight horizontal line. Then place your compass so that the pencil and the point are both on the line. Keeping the point on the line, draw a half circle and mark a dot where your half circle crosses the line.

2 Flip your compass so that the point is on the dot you marked and the pencil is now on the line. Keeping your compass at the same angle as before, draw another half circle.

3 See where the two half circles cross? Mark dots in both places. Use your ruler to connect the two dots and you're done! You can erase the two half circles now.

NOW YOU TRY!

Parallel lines

Lines that travel in the same direction and never meet are called parallel lines. When two lines are drawn perpendicular to the same line, they are always parallel to each other. Think about it – why is that true? Let's use the perpendicular lines we just drew to find out.

PARALLEL LINES!

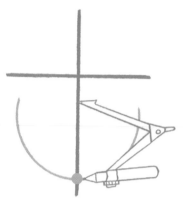

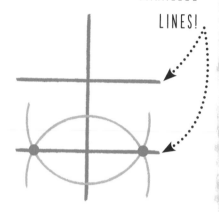

1 Set your compass so that the pencil and the point are both on the vertical line, below the horizontal line. Draw a half circle and mark a dot where the half circle crosses the line.

2 Flip your compass so that the point is on the dot and the pencil is on the line. Keeping your compass at the same angle as before, draw another half circle.

3 Mark dots in both the places where the half circles cross. Use your ruler to connect the dots!

DRAW YOUR OWN!

DRAWING WITH LINES

DUTCH PAINTER PIET MONDRIAN BECAME FAMOUS FOR HIS LOVELY PAINTINGS OF
PERPENDICULAR AND PARALLEL LINES. HE WOULD FILL A PAGE WITH LINES AND COLOUR
THE RECTANGLES THEY MADE — OFTEN IN RED, BLACK, BLUE, YELLOW AND WHITE.

Colour this picture made from perpendicular and parallel lines. Try to use the fewest colours
possible AND make sure that no two rectangles that are next to each other are the same colour.

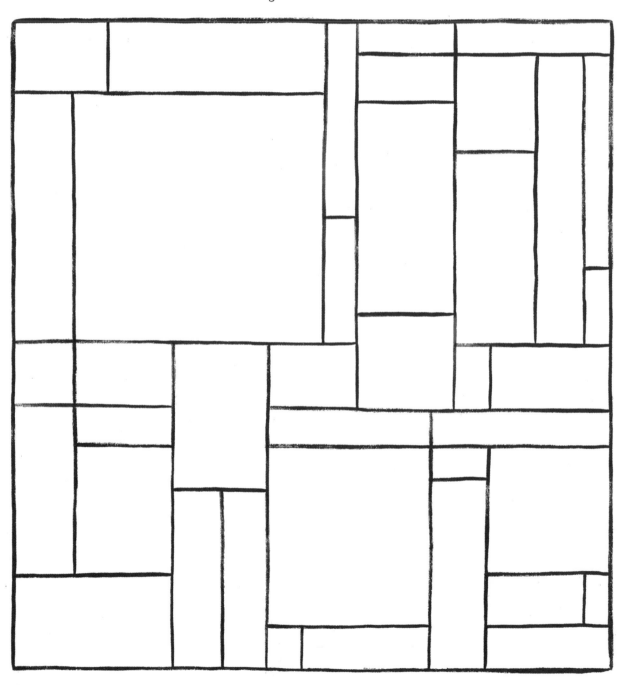

Can you do it using only four colours?
Do you think it would be possible using only three?

Now try creating your own!

LOTS OF LINKS

LET'S MAKE LINKING RECTANGLES.

1 Using a pencil, draw two overlapping rectangles that cross over each other in two places. They don't have to be perfect – any rectangles will do!

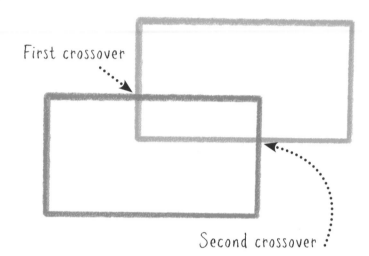

First crossover

Second crossover

2 Pick one of the rectangles to be your main shape. On the other shape, erase two small sections on either side of the first crossover. This will make an 'over' intersection. Then erase two small sections of the main rectangle on either side of the second crossover. This will make an 'under' intersection.

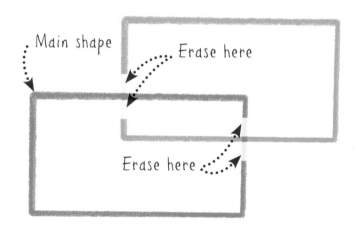

Main shape

Erase here

Erase here

3 Now decorate. You've made two linking rectangles!

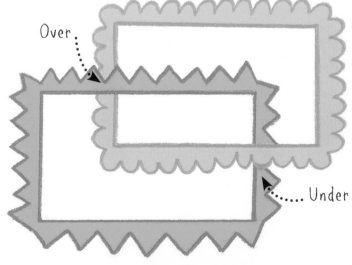

Over

Under

FILL THIS PAGE WITH LOADS OF LINKS!

Try three (or more!) rectangles. Make sure each pair is linked.

Use a pencil at first so that it's easy to erase the intersections.

Try linking circles and other shapes too!

Sneaky Squares

THERE ARE LOTS OF DIFFERENT-SIZED SQUARES HIDING IN THIS CHECKERBOARD.

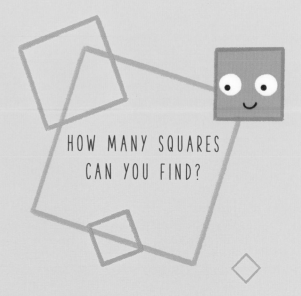

HOW MANY SQUARES
CAN YOU FIND?

HINT: If you say **64**, you've
missed a bunch!

IF YOU'RE NOT SURE WHERE TO START, TRY THIS SMALLER VERSION FIRST!

How many **DIFFERENT-SIZED** squares are hiding in this mini-checkerboard?

The 1-by-1 squares are easy to count.	How many 2-by-2 squares can you count?	And what about 3-by-3?
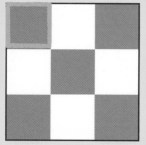	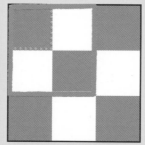	
There are NINE of those in total.	There are FOUR to find!	Just ONE this time!

DO YOU SEE ANY USEFUL NUMBER **PATTERNS?**
ONCE YOU HAVE A CLUE, TRY THE BIG CHECKERBOARD AGAIN!

DOES YOUR PATTERN WORK WITH RECTANGULAR BOARDS?

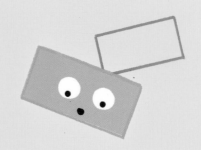

CAN YOU FIND ANY **NEW** PATTERNS?

HOW MANY SQUARES CAN YOU FIND?

REMEMBER: If a puzzle looks too tricky, start with a smaller version! ....

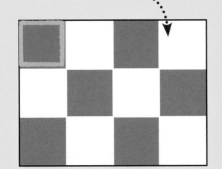

RECTANGLE CHALLENGE!

CAN YOU MAKE A **RULE** FOR HOW MANY SQUARES THERE ARE IN **ANY SIZE** RECTANGULAR CHECKERBOARD?

Need a hint? Check page 76.

SQUARE MAGIC!

WANT TO TRY SOME MYSTERIOUS MATHS?

The square below is EXACTLY the same size as the 8-by-8 grid on the opposite page. That means it has exactly the same area too. But here's the magic – if you trace and cut out the four shapes below, then throw away the small square, we bet that you can rearrange the remaining three shapes to fill the 8-by-8 grid.

Throw this piece away!

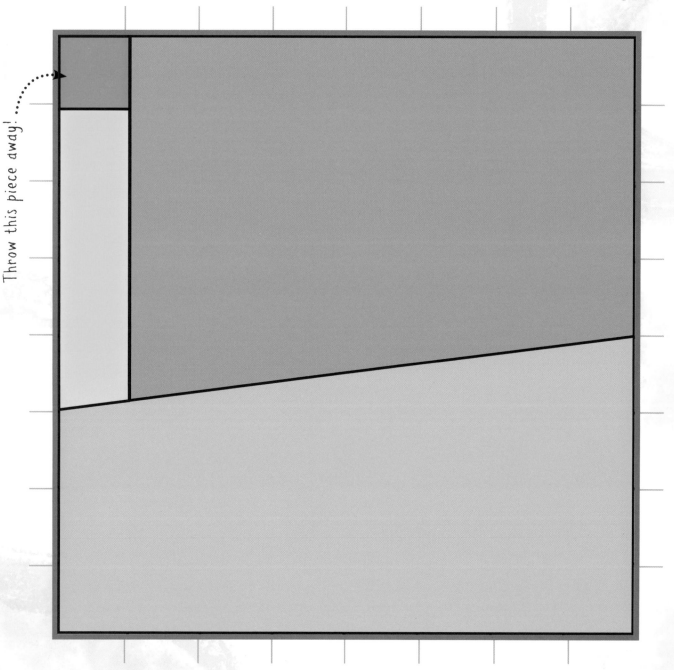

Don't believe us? Try it!

PLAY WITH THE PIECES. DO YOU SEE ANYTHING
STRANGE ABOUT HOW THEY FIT TOGETHER?

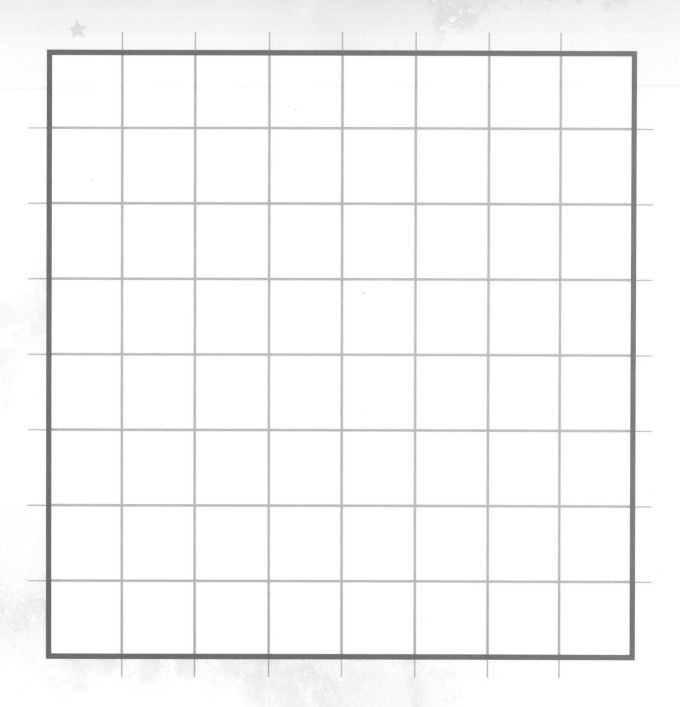

WHAT'S GOING ON HERE? THE SINGLE SQUARE SEEMS TO VANISH.
THIS SHOULDN'T WORK, BUT IT LOOKS LIKE IT DOES!

MORE SQUARE MAGIC

A SQUARE VANISHED IN THE LAST TRICK.
NOW TRY THIS TRICK TO MAKE A SQUARE APPEAR!

THE 8-BY-8 SQUARE BELOW HAS AN AREA OF 64 SQUARES.
TRACE AND CUT OUT THESE FOUR SHAPES.

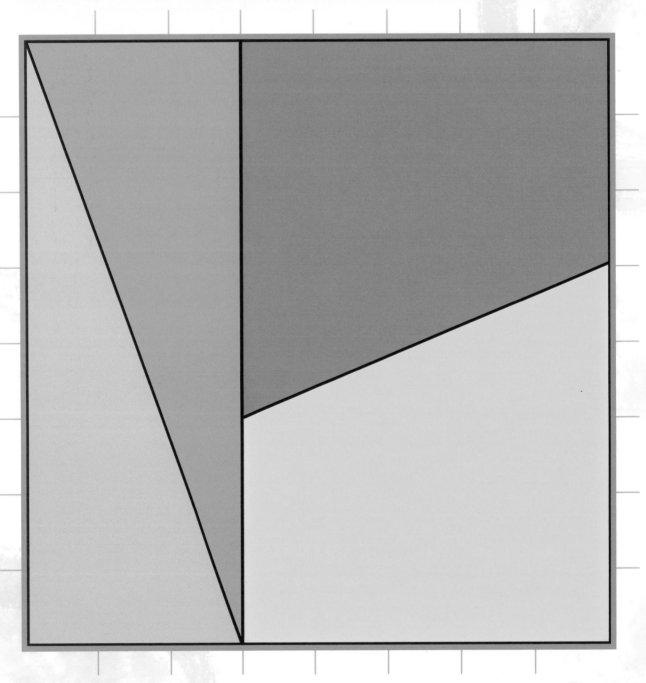

WE BET THAT YOU CAN REARRANGE
THE FOUR SHAPES TO FILL THIS
5-BY-13 RECTANGLE – WHICH HAS
AN AREA OF 65 SQUARES!

CAN THIS REALLY WORK?

MATHEMATICIANS LOVE PUZZLES WHERE
AREA SEEMS TO MAGICALLY APPEAR
AND DISAPPEAR! THEY CALL THEM
GEOMETRIC VANISHES.

CHALLENGE!

MAKE YOUR OWN GEOMETRIC
VANISH AND TRICK YOUR
FRIENDS AND FAMILY!

WONKY WORLD

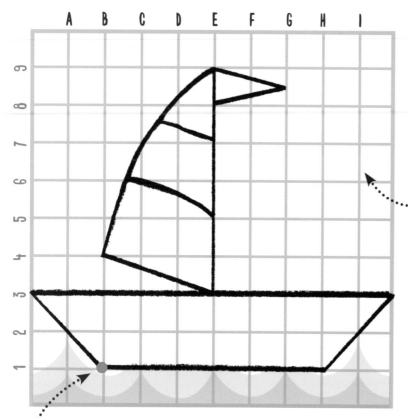

PICTURES USUALLY LOOK LIKE THEY'RE LAID OUT ON 'PERFECT' GRIDS. BUT BY USING 'WONKY', OR DISTORTED, GRIDS, YOU CAN MAKE SIMPLE DRAWINGS LOOK VERY STRANGE AND EXCITING!

Here's a scene drawn onto a perfect grid.

SEE WHAT HAPPENS TO THE SCENE WHEN YOU COPY IT ONTO THIS WAVY-LINE GRID.

Keep copying the scene until the wonky boat is finished!

Try to match corners and lines in the normal grid with corners and lines in the distorted grid.

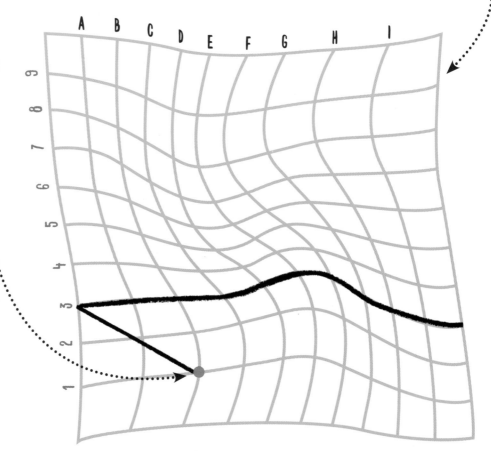

Now copy the picture onto these wonky grids!

What does your scene look like inside a crystal ball?

STRETCH!

MIRROR, MIRROR...
Let's make kaleidoscope art!

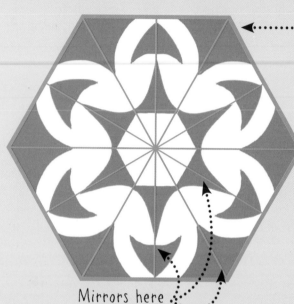

Mirrors here

This kaleidoscope pattern is made using mirror symmetry. Imagine a mirror sitting along each of the blue lines. The patterns that you see on either side of each line are reflections, or exact copies in reverse.

ADD THE REFLECTIONS TO MAKE KALEIDOSCOPE ART.

COLOUR YOUR KALEIDOSCOPE CREATIONS!

Complete the kaleidoscope pattern on the next page...

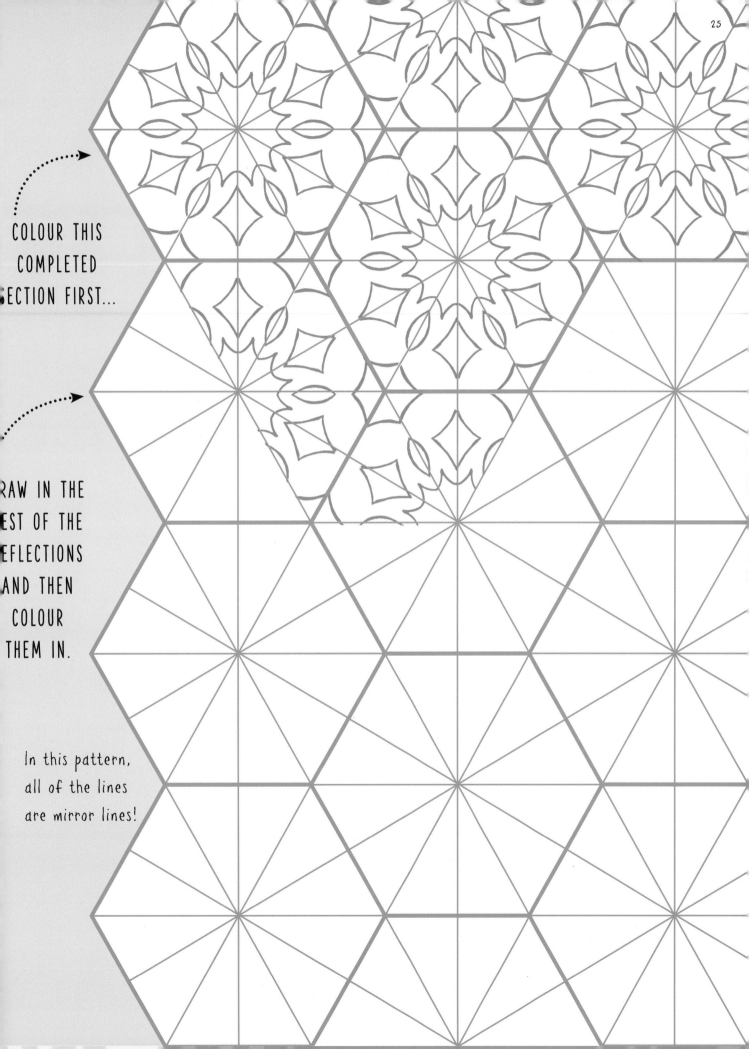

COLOUR THIS
COMPLETED
SECTION FIRST...

RAW IN THE
EST OF THE
EFLECTIONS
AND THEN
COLOUR
THEM IN.

In this pattern,
all of the lines
are mirror lines!

PERFECT POLYHEDRA

WHAT IS A POLYHEDRON?

A POLYHEDRON IS A 3D SHAPE WITH FACES THAT ARE ALL **POLYGONS** (2D SHAPES WITH STRAIGHT EDGES AND CORNERS).

WHEN YOU HAVE MORE THAN ONE POLYHEDRON, THEY'RE CALLED **POLYHEDRA.**

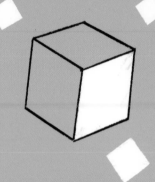

CREATE YOUR OWN COLLECTION OF POLYHEDRA USING THE NETS ON THE NEXT THREE PAGES. HERE'S HOW:

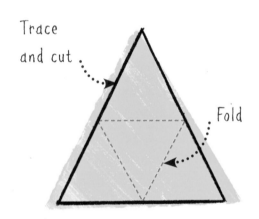

Trace and cut

Fold

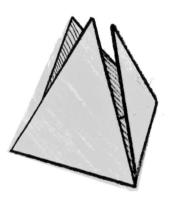

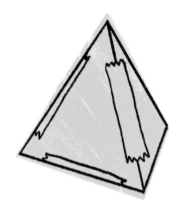

1 TRACE THE NETS FROM THE NEXT THREE PAGES AND TRANSFER THEM ONTO REGULAR PAPER. CUT ALONG THE SOLID LINES.

2 FOLD ALONG THE DASHED LINES.

3 TAPE THE EDGES TOGETHER. YOU'VE MADE A POLYHEDRON!

THE POLYHEDRA ON THESE PAGES HAVE SOMETHING IN COMMON.
CAN YOU SPOT WHAT IT IS?

A **TETRAHEDRON** IS MADE ENTIRELY FROM TRIANGLES.

Trace and cut

Fold

A **CUBE** IS MADE FROM SQUARES.

Trace and cut

Fold

You can colour your nets before folding them up! Try adding patterns too.

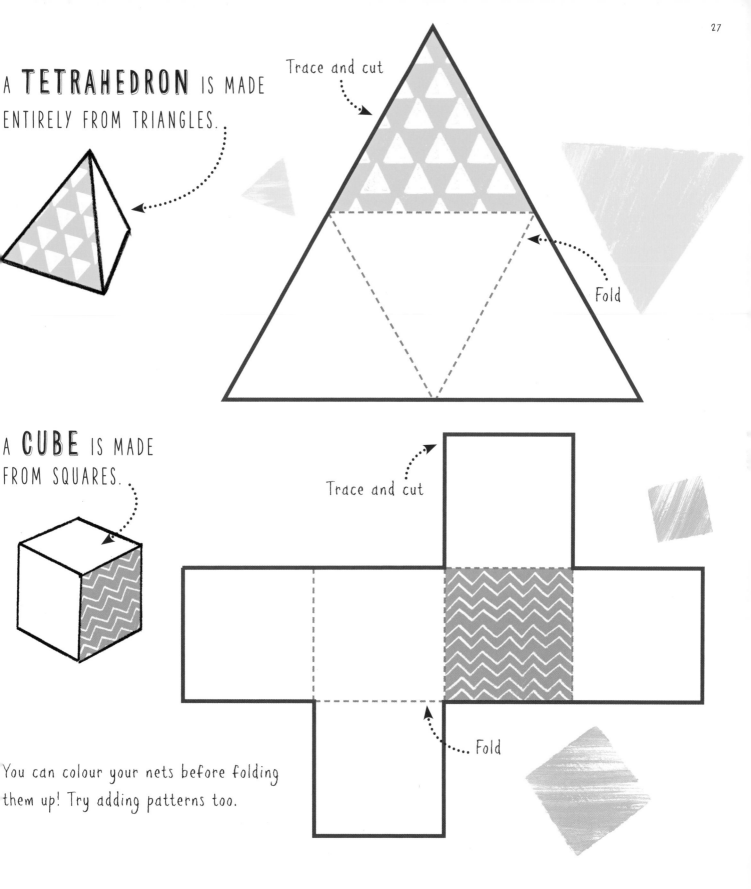

ALL OF THE 2D POLYGONS THAT MAKE UP THE FACES OF THE 3D SHAPES ARE REGULAR - THEIR SIDES AND ANGLES ARE ALL THE SAME SIZE. THESE 3D SHAPES ARE CALLED **PLATONIC SOLIDS**.

MORE PERFECT
POLYHEDRA

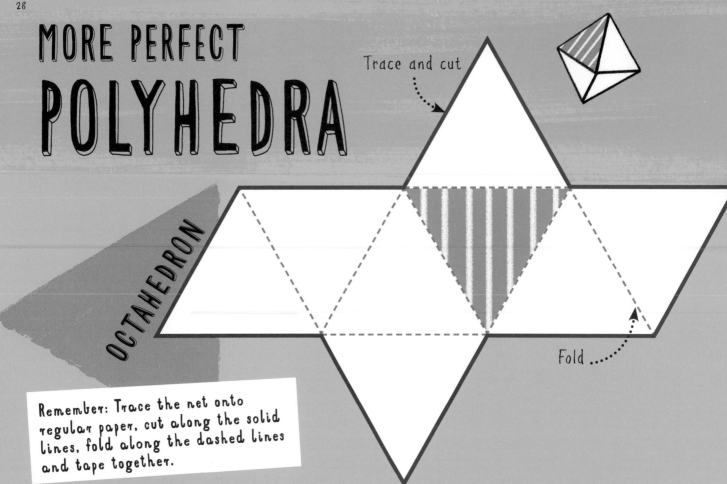

Trace and cut

OCTAHEDRON

Fold

Remember: Trace the net onto regular paper, cut along the solid lines, fold along the dashed lines and tape together.

THESE PLATONIC SOLIDS ARE A BIT HARDER TO PUT TOGETHER, BUT THEY LOOK REALLY COOL WHEN THEY'RE DONE. TRY THEM!

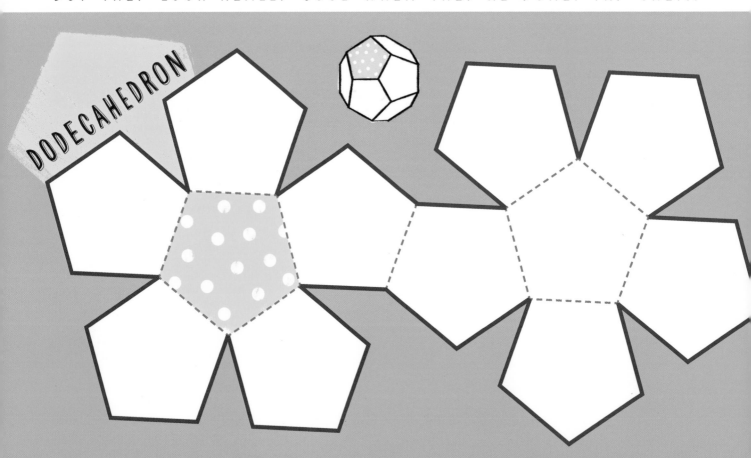

DODECAHEDRON

ICOSAHEDRON

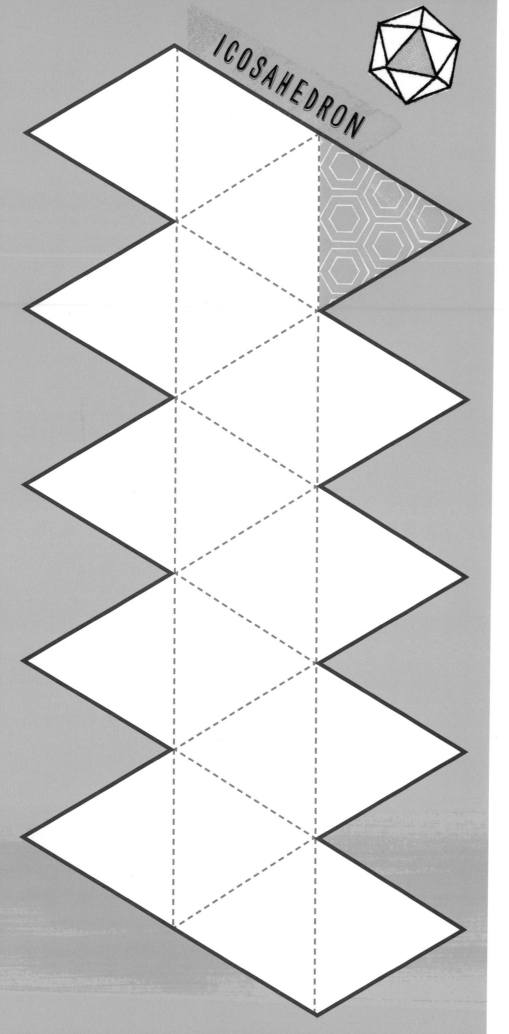

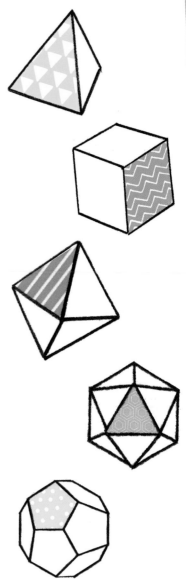

A LONG TIME AGO, A MATHEMATICIAN NAMED EUCLID PROVED THAT THERE ARE ONLY FIVE PLATONIC SOLIDS. THAT'S ALL! USE SOME BLANK PAPER AND SEE IF YOU CAN PROVE IT TOO.

TESSELLATION CUBES

TESSELLATION IS WHEN YOU COVER A FLAT SURFACE WITH A PATTERN OF SHAPES. BUT THERE'S ONE IMPORTANT RULE: THERE CAN'T BE ANY GAPS OR OVERLAPS, EVERYTHING HAS TO SLOT TOGETHER JUST RIGHT.

LET'S MAKE A CAT-COVERED CUBE...

1 Trace the triangle below, then transfer it onto regular paper and cut it out.

2 Carefully cut out the 'ear' and 'tail' from one short side of your triangle, as shown. Keep the pieces. Then cut out and keep the shape shown on the long side too.

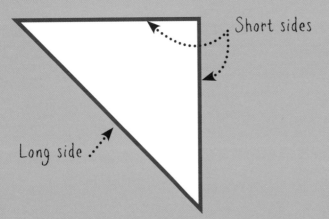

Short sides

Long side

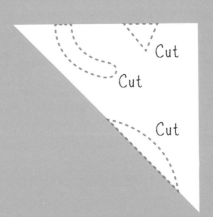

Cut

Cut

Cut

3 Tape the cut-out shapes onto the underside of your tessellation piece, as shown. Be sure to tape your shapes at the opposite points. Use a ruler for measuring if you want to be exact. You've made your tessellation piece.

4 Now decorate!

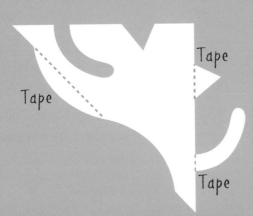

Tape

Tape

Tape

5 Next, trace the cube net below and transfer it onto regular paper. Then cut it out.

6 Place your tessellation piece on the net and draw around it. Then rotate your piece until it fits snugly with the first outline and draw around it again. Repeat the process to fill the cube!

7 Finally, add details and colour and then fold and tape the cube. All done!

Spongy Fractals

A FRACTAL IS A PATTERN MADE UP OF THE SAME GEOMETRIC SHAPE REPEATING, SMALLER AND SMALLER AND LARGER AND LARGER, FOREVER. ZOOM IN ON A PART OF THE FRACTAL AND IT LOOKS EXACTLY THE SAME AS IT DOES ZOOMED OUT.

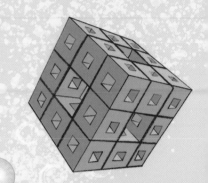

This three-dimensional fractal is called a MENGER SPONGE.

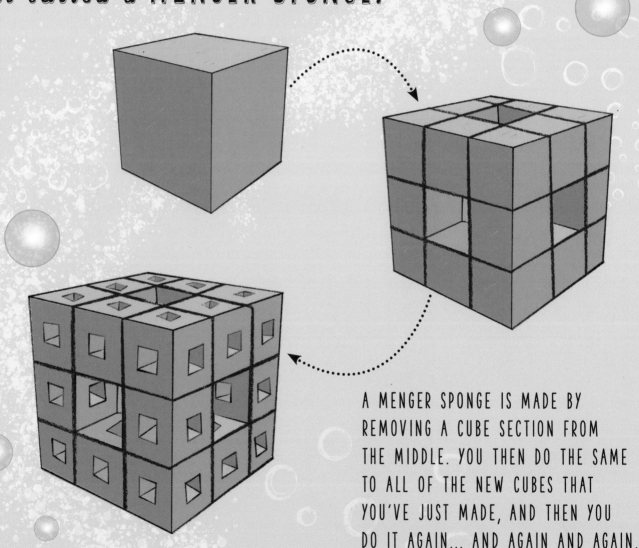

A MENGER SPONGE IS MADE BY REMOVING A CUBE SECTION FROM THE MIDDLE. YOU THEN DO THE SAME TO ALL OF THE NEW CUBES THAT YOU'VE JUST MADE, AND THEN YOU DO IT AGAIN... AND AGAIN AND AGAIN.

MAKE YOUR OWN MENGER SPONGE

1 Trace the cube net and transfer it onto regular paper. Cut it out and then fold and tape it together. Do this 20 times so that you end up with 20 cubes! For full fractal effect, draw the grid pattern on each cube face and colour in the middle square to show where cubes have been removed – do this before you start folding!

Trace and cut

Fold

2 Tape together five of your cubes to make a shape like this. Make four of these shapes.

3 Tape together the four shapes. You have built a Stage 2 Menger Sponge!

Why Stage 2? If you zoom in once, you'll see a copy of the original. If you zoom in twice, you'll see just a cube.

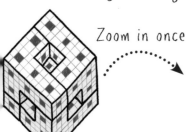

Zoom in once  Zoom in twice

CHALLENGE!

What do you think a Stage 3 Menger Sponge would look like? Can you make one?

Have a look on page 76 to see if yours looks right!

NEVER-ENDING FRACTALS

LET'S SEE WHAT ELSE WE CAN DO WITH FRACTAL PATTERNS. HOW ABOUT MAKING A FRACTAL TREE?

2 At the end of each new branch, add another pair of even smaller branches.

3 Keep repeating until you have a fractal tree!

1 Draw a tree trunk and then add two branches. At the end of each branch, draw another two branches – the same shape as the first pair, but smaller.

4 Now decorate with bark, leaves and birds.

IF YOU ADDED BRANCHES TO YOUR TREE EIGHT TIMES, HOW MANY BRANCHES WOULD YOU HAVE IN TOTAL?

Draw a fractal forest.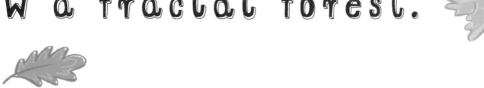

START WITH THIS TREE
AND THEN ADD MORE!

For some of your trees,
try adding three or four
branches each time
instead.

CRAZY CURVES

ALL IT TAKES TO CREATE A FASCINATING CURVE
IS A GREAT PATTERN AND A LITTLE PATIENCE.

HOW TO MAKE A
HILBERT CURVE:

Start with your shape. This is the first one:

1 Make a copy of your
shape, leaving one
square as a gap:

2 Make a second copy of your
shape, rotated 90° clockwise,
and positioned as shown:

3 Make a third copy of
your shape, rotated 90°
anticlockwise, and
positioned as shown:

4 Connect your four small
shapes into one big one!

THIS IS YOUR **NEW SHAPE**.
TO MAKE THE HILBERT CURVE, YOU NEED TO REPEAT STEPS 1-4
WITH EACH NEW SHAPE THAT YOU MAKE.

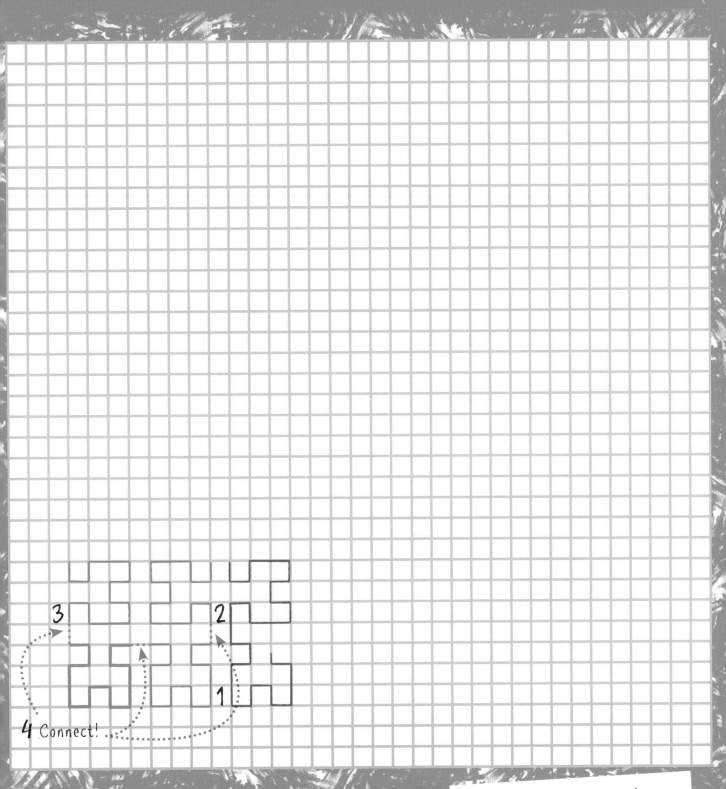

FILL THIS SPACE WITH A HILBERT CURVE, CONNECTING THE SHAPES AS YOU GO!

3

2

1

4 Connect!

WE'VE REPEATED THE FOUR STEPS FOR YOU ONCE ALREADY. NOW REPEAT THEM AGAIN WITH YOUR NEW SHAPE. THEN REPEAT AGAIN TO FILL THE PAGE! WE'VE STARTED IT FOR YOU.

To help with the rotation, draw a copy of each of your new shapes on a piece of tracing paper. Then you can turn the tracing paper and copy the rotated shape!

DRAGON CURVE

HOW TO MAKE THIS CLEVER CURVE:

1 Start with this line:
Make a copy of the line, rotated 90° clockwise, and attached to the start point of the first line.

2 Copy the new shape, rotated 90° clockwise, and attached to the end of your pattern, as shown.

Rotate and then attach here.

3 Repeat Step 2 by copying the new shape, rotated 90° clockwise, and attached to the end of your pattern.

4 Repeat again!

KEEP REPEATING TO MAKE YOUR DRAGON CURVE GROW!

This can get confusing! Try drawing a copy of your new shape on a separate piece of tracing paper each time to help with the rotation.

NOW DRAW YOUR OWN DARING DRAGON CURVE!

Start here •

Remember: For each new shape you make, rotate it 90° clockwise and attach it to the end of your pattern. It's OK if it overlaps.

You could colour in your curve using lots of different colours.

BOUNCE BOUNCE!

HAVE YOU EVER PLAYED SNOOKER, POOL OR BILLIARDS? THE PATTERN A BALL MAKES AS IT BOUNCES OFF THE SIDES OF THE TABLE IS FASCINATING!

HERE'S A 3-BY-2 TABLE.

If the ball hits the sides of this table at a 45° angle, it will leave at a 45° angle too!

WHAT PATH WILL THE BALL MAKE?

How many bounces will it take before the ball goes in another corner pocket? And which corner will it finally hit?

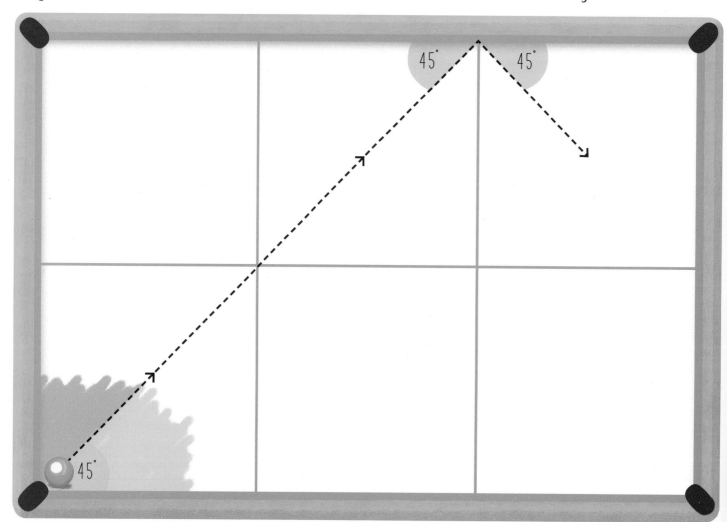

FINISH THE BOUNCE PATTERNS...

...THEN COLOUR THEM IN!

WHAT BOUNCE PATTERNS ARE MADE ON DIFFERENT-SIZED TABLES?

Try these to find out! Is there a relationship between the size of each table and its bounce pattern?

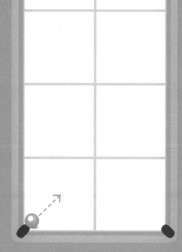

What happens to the pattern if you make the ball leave at a different angle?

Use the graph paper at the back of the book to make more bounce patterns!

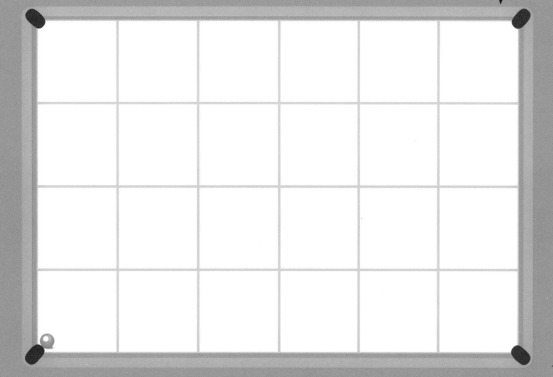

NUMBER SPIRALS

DID YOU KNOW THAT YOU CAN USE NUMBER PATTERNS TO MAKE CRAZY LOOP-DE-LOOP SPIRALS? THEY CAN START WITH ANY NUMBER.

HOW TO MAKE A SPIRAL FROM THE NUMBER 2:

1 Start with a list of the first 18 multiples of 2. See below!

2 Then find the digit sum for each multiple. The digit sum is just the digits added together.

The first four are easy.

Ten is a two-digit number, so add its digits to get the sum: 1 + 0 = 1.

NUMBERS	2	4	6	8	10	12	14	16	18	20	22	24	26	28	30	32	34	3
DIGIT SUM	2	4	6	8	1	3	5	7	9	2	4	6	8	1	3	5	7	9

SEE HOW THE DIGIT SUMS REPEAT AFTER YOU PASS 18?

Uh oh! The digits of 28 add up to 10 — a two-digit number! So, add the digits again: 1 + 0 = 1.

3 Time to draw! The digit sums tell you how long to make each line in the spiral. Start at the dot on the opposite page and draw a 2-length line heading UP. Next, draw a 4-length line heading RIGHT. Then 6 DOWN and 8 LEFT.

4 Keep following the numbers in your pattern, over and over, drawing lines UP, RIGHT, DOWN, LEFT until... you get back to the start!

Make your spiral here.

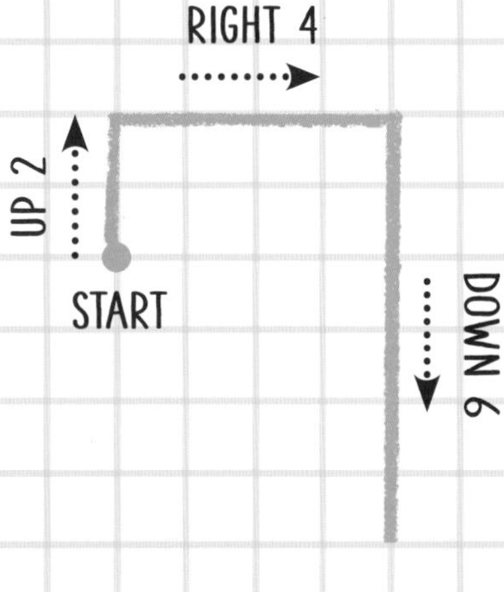

RIGHT 4

UP 2

START

DOWN 6

CAN YOU FIND ANY SYMMETRY IN YOUR SPIRAL?

MORE NUMBER SPIRALS

LET'S MAKE A SPIRAL MADE FROM THE NUMBER 8.
THE FIRST 18 MULTIPLES OF 8 ARE LISTED HERE.
FILL IN THE DIGIT SUMS AND GET DRAWING!

NUMBERS	8	16	24	32	40	48	56	64	72	80	88	96	104	112	120	128	136	144
DIGIT SUM																		

DO YOU SEE A PATTERN? THE DIGIT SUMS SHOULD REPEAT AFTER 72.

HERE ARE THE FIRST FOUR LINES
OF THE SPIRAL. KEEP IT GOING!

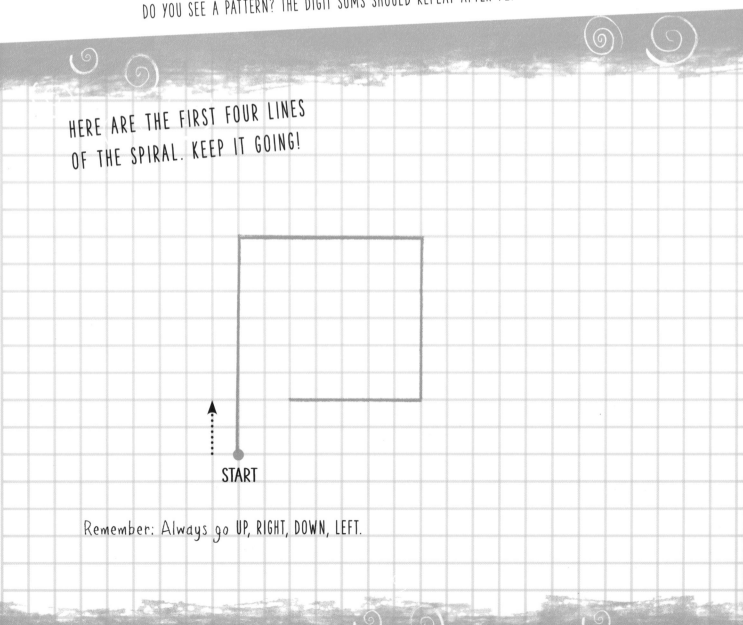

START

Remember: Always go UP, RIGHT, DOWN, LEFT.

OW LET'S TRY THE NUMBER 5...

NUMBERS	5	10	15	20	25	30	35	40	45	50	55	60	65	70	75	80	85	90
DIGIT SUM																		

THE DIGIT SUMS SHOULD REPEAT AFTER 45.

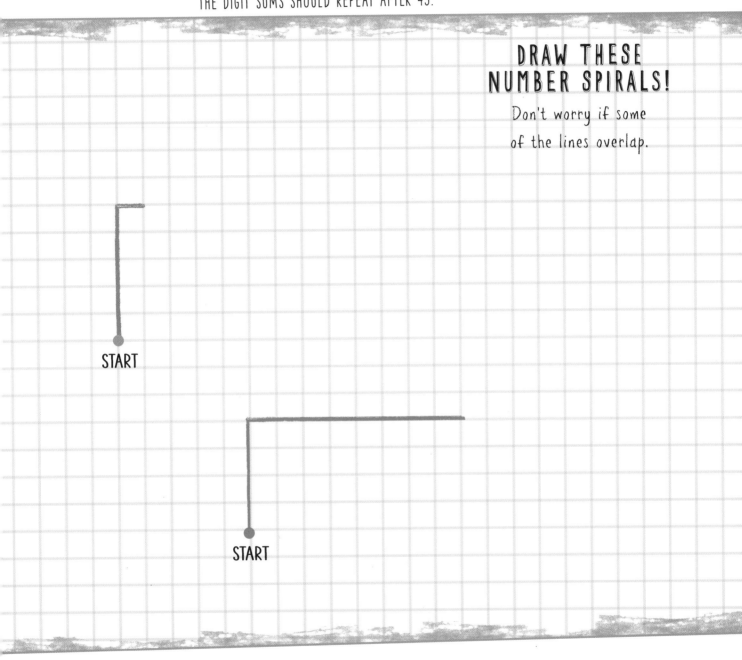

DRAW THESE NUMBER SPIRALS!

Don't worry if some
of the lines overlap.

START

START

AND THE NUMBER 4...

NUMBERS	4	8	12	16	20	24	28	32	36	40	44	48	52	56	60	64	68	72
DIGIT SUM																		

THE DIGIT SUMS SHOULD REPEAT AFTER 36.

All Tied Up in Knots

CAN YOU DRAW YOUR OWN?

Draw a squiggle...

1 MAKE SURE YOUR SQUIGGLE LOOPS ALL THE WAY ROUND, SO THAT THE BEGINNING AND THE END MEET.

2 PICK A DIRECTION TO MOVE ALONG THE SQUIGGLE AND FOLLOW IT ROUND WITH YOUR FINGER. THE FIRST TIME YOU COME TO A CROSSOVER, MAKE THE LINE YOU'RE FOLLOWING GO 'OVER' THE OTHER LINE. THEN, AT THE NEXT CROSSOVER, MAKE IT GO 'UNDER', AND SO ON. EACH TIME, ERASE A LITTLE BIT OF THE 'UNDER' LINE ON EITHER SIDE OF THE INTERSECTION TO ALLOW THE 'OVER' LINE TO CROSS.

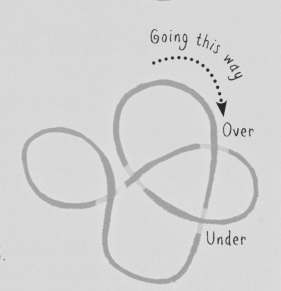

Going this way

Over

Under

3 Decorate!

YOU COULD TRY TURNING YOUR LINE INTO A PIECE OF ROPE.

Create your own knots here!

Are your knots really knotted? Do you think that you could untwist them without cutting any of the loops?

LET'S GO LOOPY!

IF YOU CAN DRAW A STAR, YOU CAN DRAW A BEAUTIFULLY SYMMETRICAL FIVE-LOOP KNOT.

How to make a five-loop knot:

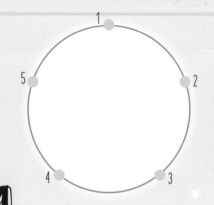

1 Use your compass to draw a circle. Add five dots around the edge. Try to space the dots evenly.

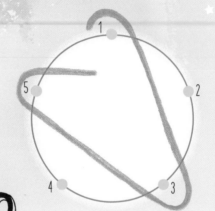

2 Starting at dot 1, connect every second dot by drawing a wide loop around it.

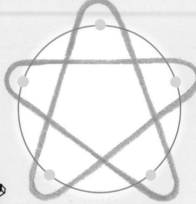

3 Keep connecting until you get back to where you started.

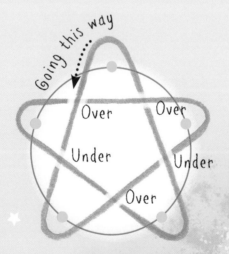

Going this way

Over   Over

Under   Under

Over

4 Pick a direction to move around the knot. At the first crossover, make the line you are following go 'over'. Then, at the next crossover, make it go 'under', and so on. Each time, erase a little bit of the 'under' line on either side, to allow the 'over' line to cross. Once you've finished, erase the circle.

5 DECORATE!

Draw your own knotted star!

Use a pencil at first so you can
erase the small sections and the
circle once you're ready to decorate!

MORE LOOPY KNOTS

Try a seven-loop knot.

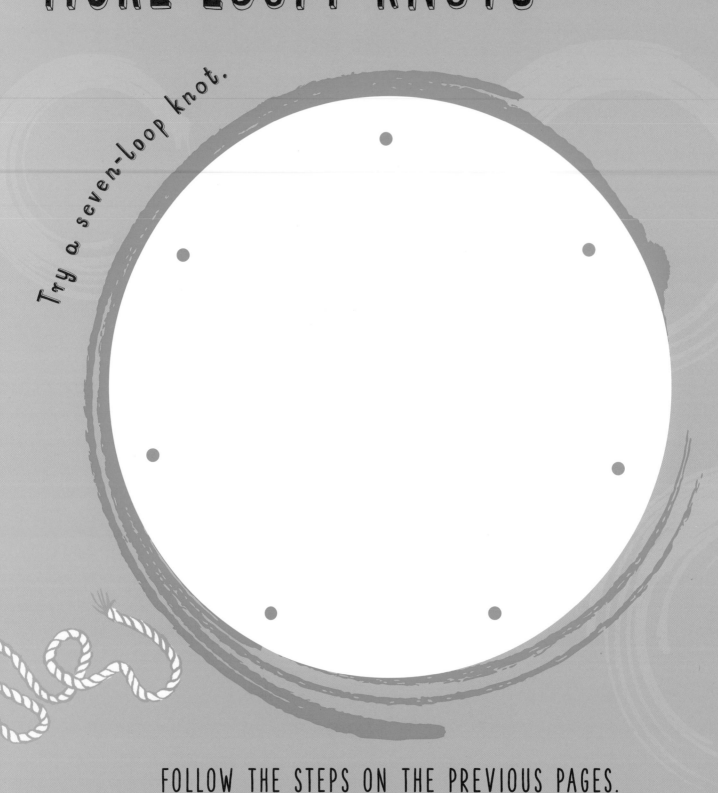

FOLLOW THE STEPS ON THE PREVIOUS PAGES.
CONNECT EVERY SECOND DOT.

Try a nine-loop knot next.

CONNECT EVERY SECOND DOT.

DRAWING WITH DOMINOES

In maths, a **domino** is a shape made of two squares attached edge to edge. This is it:

A **tromino** is a shape made of three squares attached edge to edge. There are two types of **trominoes**:

A **polyomino** is a shape made of any number of squares attached along their edges.

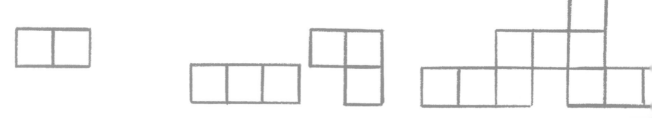

THERE ARE FIVE TYPES OF **TETROMINOES** (FOUR SQUARES ATTACHED EDGE TO EDGE). ONE OF THEM IS BELOW – CAN YOU MAKE THE OTHER FOUR?

Once you've found the other four, see if you can make a domino path out of tetrominoes by adding dots onto each square. The touching squares of each tile should always have the same number of dots.

HOW MANY DIFFERENT PENTOMINOES
(FIVE SQUARES ATTACHED EDGE TO EDGE) CAN YOU MAKE?

Once you've had a go,
check the next page to see
if you've found them all.

SOME HEXOMINOES (SIX SQUARES) CAN BE
FOLDED UP INTO CUBES. CAN YOU FIND THEM ALL?

A hexomino that folds into a cube
is also called a cube net.

PENTOMINO PUZZLES

A PENTOMINO IS A SHAPE MADE OF FIVE SQUARES ATTACHED EDGE TO EDGE. THEY MAKE GREAT PUZZLE PIECES! TRACE THE 12 SHAPES BELOW AND CUT THEM OUT. CAN YOU USE THEM TO FILL THE TWO RECTANGLES BELOW? ONLY USE EACH SHAPE ONCE AND NO GAPS ALLOWED!

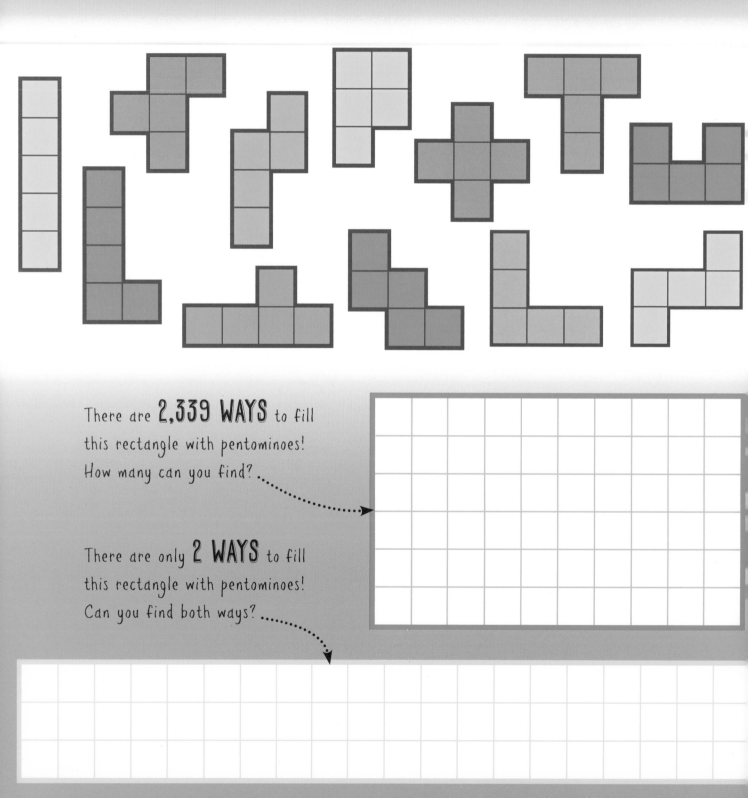

There are **2,339 WAYS** to fill this rectangle with pentominoes! How many can you find?

There are only **2 WAYS** to fill this rectangle with pentominoes! Can you find both ways?

Puzzle pictures

USE YOUR PENTOMINO PUZZLE
PIECES TO COMPLETE THE TWO
ANIMAL PICTURES. ONCE YOU'VE
SLOTTED THE PIECES IN, DRAW
AROUND THE EDGE OF EACH ONE
AND THEN COLOUR IN YOUR
PENTOMINO CREATURES.

You only need to use **9** of your
puzzle pieces for this one.

Use all **12** pieces here.
We've done some for you!

Perfect Paper POLYGONS

PAPER NORMALLY COMES IN RECTANGLES – BUT DON'T LET THAT STOP YOUR CREATIVITY! USING SYMMETRY AND A LITTLE FOLDING AND CUTTING, YOU CAN TURN A RECTANGULAR PIECE OF PAPER INTO ANY POLYGON!

LET'S START BY MAKING A **SQUARE**. THIS ONE IS SUPER-EASY! YOU CAN USE ANY RECTANGULAR SHEET OF PAPER.

1 FOLD THE RECTANGLE DIAGONALLY, LINING UP ONE SHORTER EDGE WITH ONE LONGER EDGE.

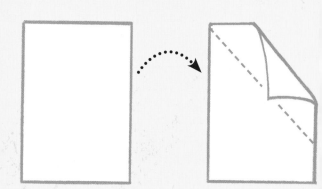

2 SEE THE SKINNY STRIP OF PAPER LEFT AT THE BOTTOM? CUT IT OFF.

UNFOLD THE PAPER...

ALL DONE! YOU'VE TRANSFORMED A REGULAR RECTANGLE INTO A SQUARE. SIMPLE!

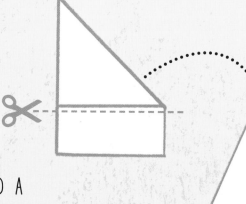

THE POLYGON POSSIBILITIES ARE ENDLESS!

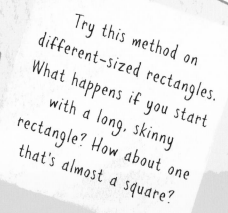

Try this method on different-sized rectangles. What happens if you start with a long, skinny rectangle? How about one that's almost a square?

NOW THAT YOU CAN MAKE A SQUARE, TRY FOLDING AND CUTTING IT INTO A NEW SHAPE.

LET'S MAKE AN **OCTAGON.**
YOU CAN USE ANY SQUARE PIECE OF PAPER.

1 FOLD THE SQUARE IN HALF DIAGONALLY TO MAKE A TRIANGLE.

2 FOLD THE TRIANGLE IN HALF TO MAKE A SMALLER TRIANGLE.

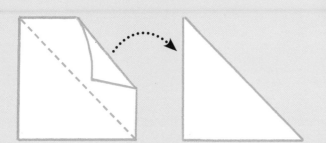

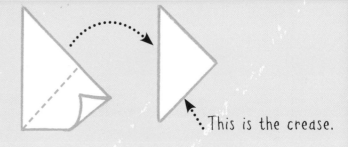

This is the crease.

3 FOLD THE SMALL TRIANGLE IN HALF ONE LAST TIME!

4 WITH THE CREASED SIDE AT THE BOTTOM, TURN THE TRIANGLE CLOCKWISE SLIGHTLY. CUT DIAGONALLY ACROSS AS SHOWN, JUST BELOW THE CORNER.

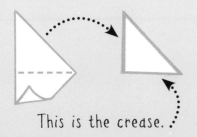

This is the crease.

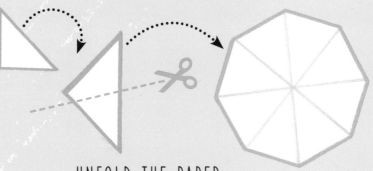

UNFOLD THE PAPER...

TAH-DAH! YOU'VE MADE AN OCTAGON.

Tip: If your octagon ends up looking more like a square, try playing with the angle of your cut.

CHALLENGE!
CAN YOU FOLD AND CUT A SQUARE INTO A HEXADECAGON (16-SIDED SHAPE)?

More Perfect POLYGONS

MAKE A HEXAGON.

THIS TIME YOU'LL NEED A PROTRACTOR! START WITH A RECTANGLE.
YOU CAN TRACE THE TEMPLATE ON PAGE 77 AND CUT IT OUT IF YOU LIKE.

1 FOLD YOUR RECTANGLE IN HALF.

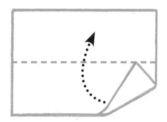

2 FOLD IT IN HALF AGAIN TO FIND THE CENTRE OF THE CREASED EDGE AND THEN OPEN IT OUT.

3 SET YOUR PROTRACTOR IN THE CENTRE. MEASURE AND DRAW TWO LINES, AS SHOWN. EACH LINE SHOULD BE 60° APART.

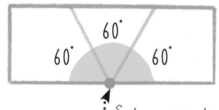

Set your protractor here.

4 NEXT, FOLD ALONG THE LINES.

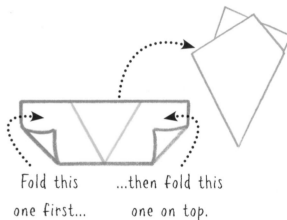

Fold this one first...   ...then fold this one on top.

5 NOW CUT STRAIGHT ACROSS THE TOP.

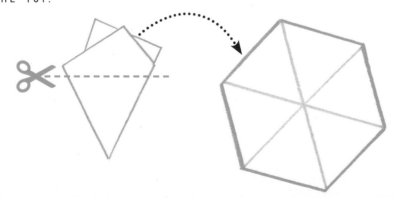

UNFOLD THE PAPER...

HEY PRESTO!
YOU'VE MADE A HEXAGON!

HOW ABOUT A **STAR**?
THIS SHAPE IS A LITTLE MORE TRICKY!

YOU'LL NEED A PROTRACTOR FOR THIS POLYGON TOO.
START WITH A RECTANGLE. YOU CAN TRACE AND CUT OUT THE TEMPLATE ON PAGE 77.

1 FOLD YOUR RECTANGLE IN HALF.

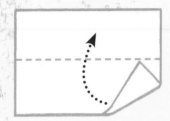

2 FOLD IT IN HALF AGAIN TO FIND THE CENTRE OF THE CREASED EDGE AND THEN OPEN IT OUT.

3 SET YOUR PROTRACTOR IN THE CENTRE. MEASURE AND DRAW FOUR LINES, AS SHOWN. EACH LINE SHOULD BE 36° APART.

36° 36° 36° 36° 36°

Set your protractor here.

4 FOLD ALONG THE LINES FROM LEFT TO RIGHT.

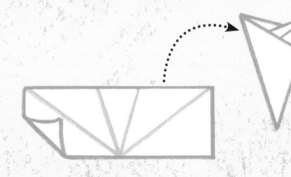

5 ALMOST DONE! THIS TIME CUT STRAIGHT ON A REALLY STEEP DIAGONAL.

UNFOLD THE PAPER...
TAH-DAH! YOU'VE MADE A FIVE-POINTED STAR!

Let It SNOW, Let It SNOW

MAKE A FLURRY OF BEAUTIFUL PAPER SNOWFLAKES!

1 Start with a square. Fold the square in half diagonally to make a triangle.

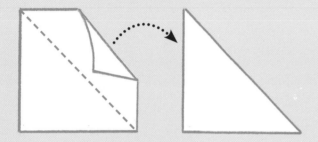

2 Fold the triangle in half again to make a smaller triangle.

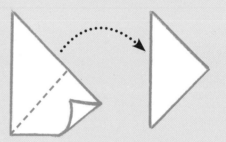

3 Fold the smaller triangle in half one last time!

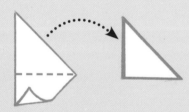

4 Now rotate your triangle clockwise and draw on your snowflake design. You can copy this one or make up your own.

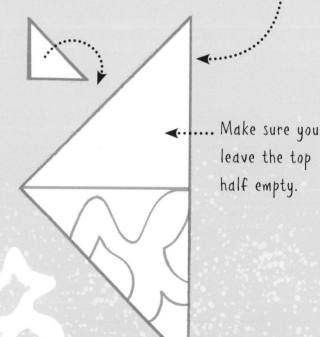

Make sure you leave the top half empty.

5 Cut off the top half of the triangle and then cut out the pattern. You're ready to unfold your snowflake!

Cut along the dashed lines.

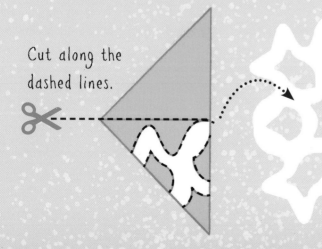

TRY COPYING THESE PATTERNS TO MAKE YOUR OWN COLLECTION OF PAPER SNOWFLAKES, OR MAKE UP YOUR OWN DESIGNS!

HEXAGONAL snowflakes

DID YOU KNOW THAT REAL SNOWFLAKES HAVE SIX-FOLD SYMMETRY? THAT MEANS THAT THEY HAVE SIX AXES OF SYMMETRY AND THE BEST SNOWFLAKES ARE MADE FROM PERFECT HEXAGONS!

START WITH A RECTANGLE. YOU CAN TRACE AND CUT OUT THE TEMPLATE ON PAGE 77.

1 Fold your rectangle in half. Then fold it in half again and open out to find the centre of the folded edge.

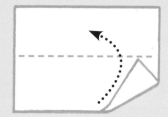

2 Use your protractor to measure and draw two lines, as shown. All three angles need to be **60°**.

Set your protractor here.

3 Fold along the lines.

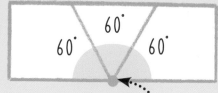

Fold this one first...   ...then fold this one on top.

4 Draw on your snowflake design. Copy this one or create your own!

... You can leave the top half empty.

5 Cut off the top section, cut out the pattern and unfold your snowflake!

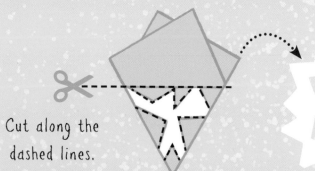

Cut along the dashed lines.

COPY THESE PATTERNS OR MAKE UP YOUR OWN!

PUZZLE PIECES

HERE'S A CHALLENGE FOR YOU... CAN YOU BREAK THESE SHAPES
INTO SMALLER PIECES THAT ARE ALL THE SAME SIZE AND SHAPE?

BREAK THIS SHAPE INTO FOUR SAME-SIZE,
SAME-SHAPE PIECES! ......

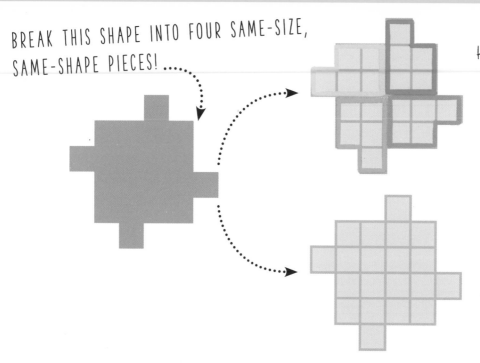

Here's one way
to do it!

There's another way to do
it too — try to find it!

Draw on your shape in pencil.
If it doesn't work, you can
erase it and try again.

SHAPES THAT ARE THE SAME SIZE AND SHAPE ARE CALLED **CONGRUENT.**

NEXT, BREAK THIS SHAPE INTO
FOUR CONGRUENT PIECES. ......

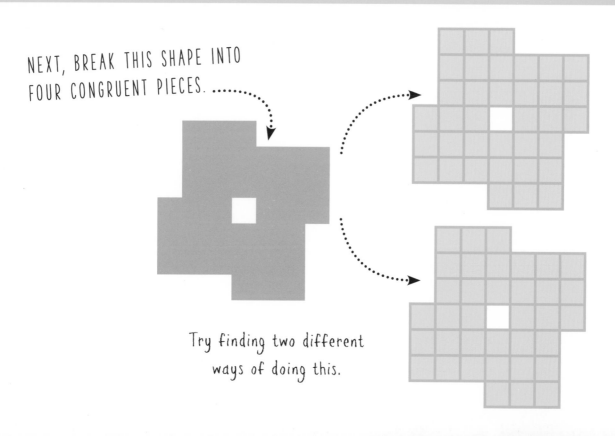

Try finding two different
ways of doing this.

Now try these!

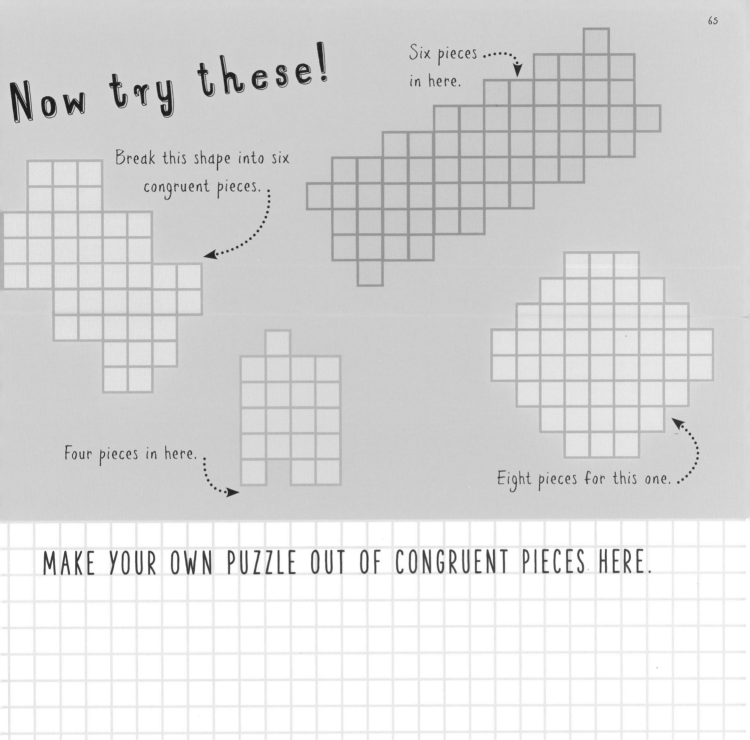

Six pieces ...... in here.

Break this shape into six congruent pieces.

Four pieces in here.

Eight pieces for this one.

MAKE YOUR OWN PUZZLE OUT OF CONGRUENT PIECES HERE.

SCISSOR SUPERPOWERS!

DID YOU KNOW THAT WITH SOME CLEVER FOLDING AND JUST **ONE** CUT, YOU CAN MAKE ANY SHAPE YOU WANT FROM A SIMPLE SQUARE OF PAPER?

With just one cut of your scissors, you can make this shape out of a square piece of paper.

X MARKS THE SPOT!

HERE'S HOW:

1 Start with a square. Fold the paper in half diagonally, to make a triangle.

2 Fold the triangle in half.

3 Then fold it in half again!

4 Rotate the triangle as shown, then fold the largest angle (it's a right angle) up and above the opposite side. Your paper should look like a boat!

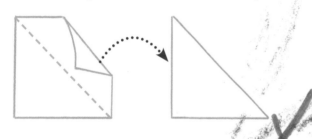

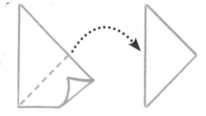

5 Time to cut! Cut off the top of the boat. Unfold...

DONE!

HOW ABOUT A DOUBLE ARROW?

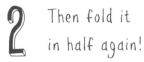

1 Start with a square. Fold it in half diagonally, to make a triangle.

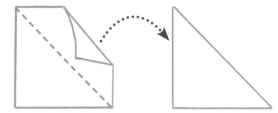

2 Then fold it in half again!

3 Rotate the triangle as shown, then fold the largest angle (the right angle) up – but this time stop when it just meets the opposite side.

4 Time to cut! Starting on the folded side, make a diagonal cut that is parallel to the opposite side of the folded-up triangle. Unfold...

TAH-DAH!
YOU'VE MADE A DOUBLE ARROW WITH JUST ONE CUT!

NOW TRY THESE! ALL YOU NEED IS **ONE SNIP!**

Can you make these two frame shapes?

HINT: Fold the paper in half first... but not diagonally.

Double hexagon

HINT: Fold to make a rectangle, then a square, then a rectangle again!

HINT: Fold to make a triangle, then fold your triangle into a square. Then fold your square into a triangle again!

Six-pointed star

HINT: Start folding a hexagon...

If it's tricky, try sketching the image on your paper before you fold.

CIRCLE CONNECTIONS

Next, draw a line from 1 to 3. Then draw a line from 2 to 5. And then from 3 to 7, 4 to 9, 5 to 11... See the pattern?

DRAW A LINE FROM 0 TO 1.

As the start number goes up by 1, the end number goes up by 2! Keep adding lines until you have gone right around the circle. What shape have you made?

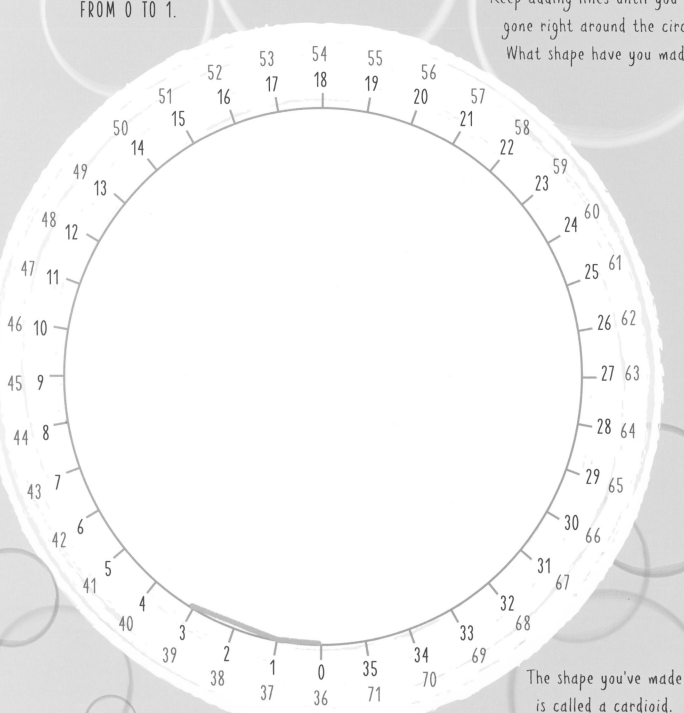

The shape you've made is called a cardioid.

How about a figure 8?

FOR THIS SHAPE, YOU NEED NUMBERS UP TO 107!

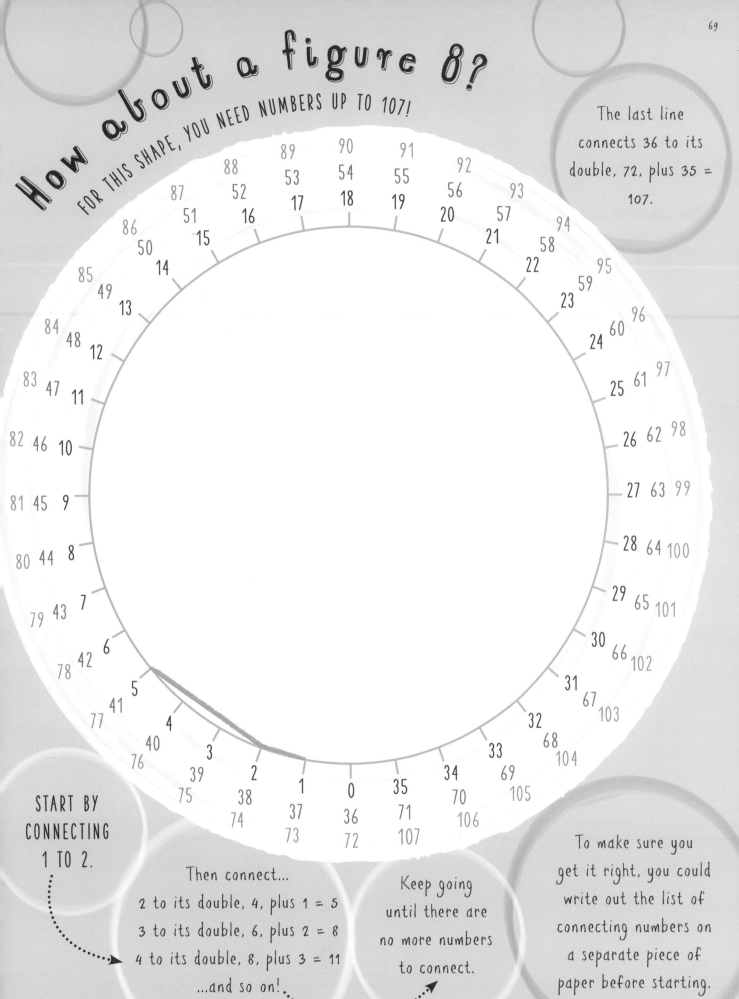

The last line connects 36 to its double, 72, plus 35 = 107.

START BY CONNECTING 1 TO 2.

Then connect...
2 to its double, 4, plus 1 = 5
3 to its double, 6, plus 2 = 8
4 to its double, 8, plus 3 = 11
...and so on!

Keep going until there are no more numbers to connect.

To make sure you get it right, you could write out the list of connecting numbers on a separate piece of paper before starting.

WOVEN WONDERS

YOU DON'T NEED STRAW OR WOOL TO MAKE A BEAUTIFUL WEAVING
– YOUR COLOURING PENS, PAPER AND A PATTERN WILL DO THE TRICK!

REPEAT THESE PATTERNS TO MAKE WOVEN DRAWINGS...

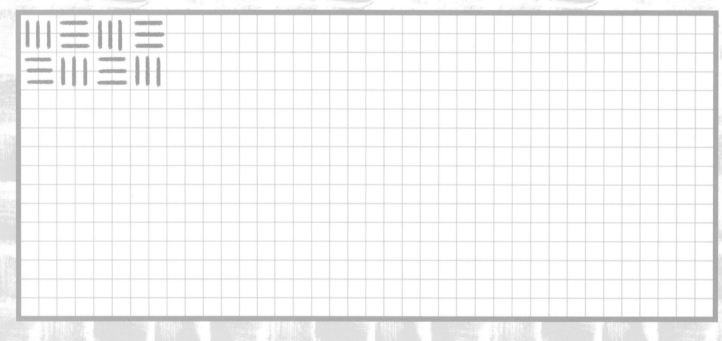

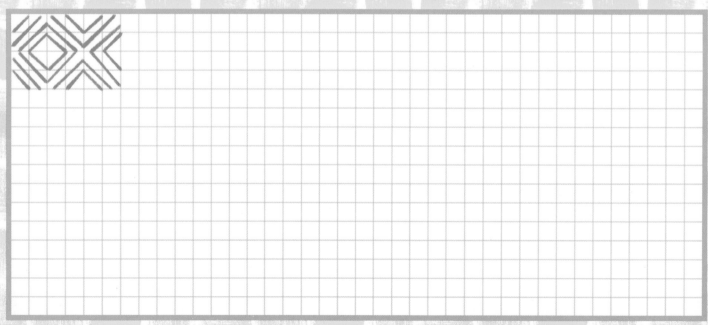

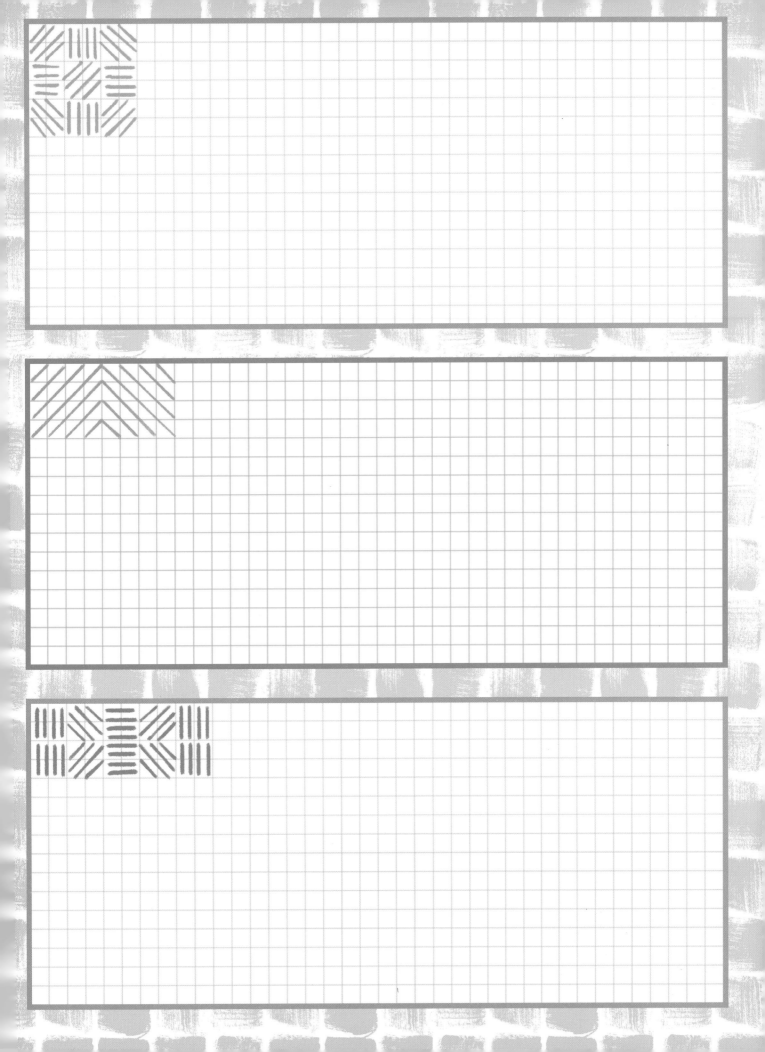

TAKE IT FURTHER

Not ready to stop? Here are some ideas for more smart art projects.

IDEAS FOR PROJECTS

Pages 26-29 show you how to make all five platonic solids. Did you know that platonic solids make great dice? Most dice are made from cubes, but you can use tetrahedra, octahedra, dodecahedra and icosahedra to make four-, eight-, twelve- and twenty-sided dice! Use some in your next dice game.

Make greeting cards out of paper snowflakes (pages 60-63). Cut out some snowflakes and glue them to the front of a card. Every snowflake card is unique!

Paper polygons (pages 56-59) make beautiful tiles! Cut some out from different colours of paper and piece them together to make a lovely paper pattern. Or cut them from cloth or felt and sew them together to make a quilt!

If you can draw a crazy curve (pages 36-39), you can make a crazy maze! Add some extra lines and obstacles to your Hilbert or Dragon curve to make a tricky maze.

After filling in the wonky grids (pages 22-23), you can try drawing a grid onto a ball and copying a picture onto it.

TRY SOMETHING NEW

On pages 10-11, you learned how to draw parallel and perpendicular lines using a compass and a ruler. What else can you make with your compass and ruler? Can you use just those two tools to make a perfect square? How about a triangle with three equal sides?

In the Sneaky Squares activity (pages 16-17), you counted the number of squares hiding in square and rectangular grids. But grids can also be triangular! (See the graph paper at the back of the book.) Can you do the same challenge, but with a grid of triangles?

Did you notice that the kaleidoscope on pages 24-25 is made using hexagons? You can use many other shapes to make a kaleidoscope. All you need is a shape or group of shapes that completely fill a flat space in a repeating pattern! Try using squares or a combination of squares and triangles. What other kaleidoscope patterns can you make?

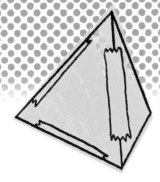

In the Perfect Polyhedra activity on pages 26–29, you made all five of the platonic solids (the three-dimensional shapes made out of identical regular polygons, with the same number of polygons meeting at each corner). But there are many, many more polyhedra out there! Try making polyhedra using two or more different shapes. Can you make a polyhedron out of just squares and triangles? How about pentagons, squares and triangles?

The polyominoes on pages 52–55 are made using squares. Can you make polyominoes from other shapes? Use the triangular graph paper at the back of the book to try making some from triangles. What other shapes can you use?

BEYOND DRAWING

On pages 32–33, you made a Menger Sponge out of paper. But you can make one out of anything that can be made into a cube! Try making one using cube building blocks, toothpicks and paper, clay, sugar cubes... your imagination is the limit!

Make circle connections (pages 68–69) using coloured wool or string! Or draw them on clear plastic or glass and paint the empty spaces with bright colours to make beautiful stained glass.

You can draw great fractal trees on paper (pages 34–35). How about making them in 3D? Use sticks, straws or toothpicks to make a 3D fractal tree forest! Decorate your trees with paper leaves, birds and flowers.

In the Bounce Bounce! activity on pages 40–41, you drew the patterns made by a ball as it bounces around a table. But do bouncing balls do that in real life? Try it!

Drawing knots (pages 46–51) is fun – but how about tying them? Try to tie the knots you drew using real string or rope.

GLOSSARY

2D: a flat shape without thickness, just height and width, such as a drawing of a square.

3D: an object that has height, width and depth, like something in the real world; also known as a solid shape.

ANGLE: the space, measured in <u>degrees</u>, between two lines that meet in a single point.

AXIS (OF SYMMETRY): a line that divides a <u>symmetrical</u> shape or object in half. If you folded a symmetrical shape along its axis, the two halves would match.

CARDIOID: a curve shape that looks like a heart, made from overlapping circles.

COMPASS: a drawing tool used for making perfect circles.

CONGRUENT: two shapes that are exactly the same size and shape.

CUBE NET: a hexomino that folds into a cube.

DEGREE: the unit of measurement used for measuring <u>angles</u>.

DIGIT SUM: the sum of all a number's <u>digits</u>, for example, 41 would be (4 + 1 = 5), making 5 the digit sum.

DIGIT: a single number from 0 to 9, used in writing a number. For example, 28 has 2 digits: 2 and 8.

DISTORT: to change the natural or original shape of something, such as a <u>grid</u>, so that it doesn't look 'normal'.

FRACTAL: a shape or <u>pattern</u> that repeats itself forever. Each part is made up of a scaled-down version of the whole shape.

GEOMETRIC VANISH: a type of puzzle in which a trick makes it look like areas of shapes vanish or appear.

GEOMETRY: the area of maths that looks at points, lines, shapes and space.

GRID: a background covering a flat space made from crossing lines. Grids often have squares, but they can have triangles or hexagons too.

HORIZONTAL: the word that describes a line that extends from side to side.

INTERSECTION: the point where two or more lines meet or cross.

KALEIDOSCOPE PATTERN: a vibrant, geometric design that uses the mathematical rules of <u>symmetry</u> to create a <u>pattern</u>.

KNOT: in maths, a closed loop that might have twists in it. A real knot has twists that can't be undone without cutting the loop.

MENGER SPONGE: a type of <u>3D</u> <u>fractal</u> made of cubes arranged in a <u>pattern</u> that looks like a sponge.

MIRROR SYMMETRY: when an object and its <u>reflection</u> share an edge (this can be with a mirror or if it is drawn, for example) and the two resulting images look the same; they 'mirror', or reflect, each other.

MULTIPLE (OF): a number is a multiple of a second number if the first can be divided perfectly by the second. For example, six is a multiple

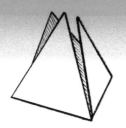

of three because six divided by three is two.

NET: a 2D drawing or pattern that you can cut and fold to make a 3D model.

PARALLEL LINES: two lines that travel in the same direction and always stay the same distance apart (they never meet).

PATTERN: a repeated decorative design or a set of numbers, shapes, or other objects that have been arranged according to a mathematical rule.

PERPENDICULAR LINES: two lines that cross each other at a 90-degree (right) angle.

PLATONIC SOLID: a 3D shape where all the 'faces', or sides, are made of the same regular polygon. There are five platonic solids: tetrahedrons (formed of four triangular faces – a pyramid shape); cubes (six-faced squares, such as normal dice); octahedrons (eight faces, seen in a diamond shape); dodecahedrons (12 faces); and icosahedrons (20 faces).

POLYGON: a 2D shape made out of straight lines meeting in angles. These include: triangles (three-sided shapes); squares and rectangles (four-sided shapes); pentagons (five); hexagons (six); heptagons (seven); and octagons (eight).

POLYHEDRON (plural polyhedra): a 3D shape made out of polygonal faces.

POLYOMINO: a shape made of squares joined together at their edges. These include: dominoes (two squares joined together at their edges); trominoes (three); tetrominoes (four); pentominoes (five); and hexominoes (six).

PROTRACTOR: a tool used to measure and draw angles.

REFLECTION: see 'Mirror symmetry'.

REGULAR POLYGON: a type of polygon with sides that are all the same length and angles that are all the same size.

ROTATION: turning a shape around a point, such as one of its corners.

SOLID SHAPE: see '3D'.

SPIRAL: a curved line that circles around from a fixed point. A spiral gets bigger or smaller as it moves away from the fixed point.

SYMMETRY: a shape has symmetry if it does not look different when it is moved in a particular way, such as when it is reflected or rotated.

TESSELLATION: a repeating pattern of shapes. It has no gaps or overlaps.

THREE-DIMENSIONAL: see '3D'.

TWO-DIMENSIONAL: see '2D'.

VERTICAL: the word that describes a line that extends up and down.

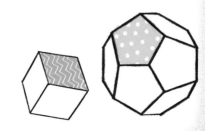

HINTS AND ANSWERS

Page 17: Rectangle challenge!

If your rectangular checkerboard has dimensions m-by-n, then you can always fit m 1-by-1 squares across one side and n 1-by-1 squares across the other side. That means that m times n 1-by-1 squares fit in any rectangle. How many 2-by-2 squares can you fit along each side? Not quite so many! In fact, you can fit exactly one less. So, how many 2-by-2 squares does that mean you can fit all together?

(P.S. m and n are just numbers, but since we want a pattern for a rectangle of any size, we want to leave our options open!)

Page 33: Make your own Menger Sponge

Here's what a Stage 3 Menger Sponge looks like. ·······

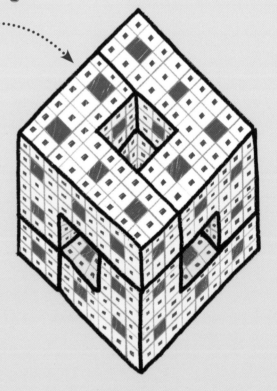

Rectangle Template